Co-ordinated SCIENCE
Physics
Activities

Stephen Pople

Oxford University Press

Oxford University Press, Walton Street, Oxford OX2 6DP
Oxford New York Toronto
Delhi Bombay Calcutta Madras Karachi
Petaling Jaya Singapore Hong Kong Tokyo
Nairobi Dar es Salaam Cape Town
Melbourne Auckland
and associated companies in
Berlin Ibadan

Oxford is a trade mark of Oxford University Press

ISBN 0 19 914285 8

Typeset by Tradespools Ltd, Frome
**Printed in Great Britain by
Scotprint Limited, Musselburgh**

Contents

Introduction

In this book, you'll find a wide range of experiments and other activities based on experimental work. You are most likely to find them useful if you are following a GCSE course in physics or taking physics as part of a GCSE co-ordinated science course. The activities will help you to develop your experimental skills. They may also be used by your teacher to assess your skill in:

designing and carrying out experiments
following instructions
using apparatus
making measurements
handling data
presenting results
drawing conclusions

The book is divided into sections:

- **Experiments** starts by telling you how to tackle experiments, how to use equipment and how to present your results. Next come the experiments themselves. Step-by-step instructions tell you what to do, though there's still plenty for you to think out for yourself! With each experiment, there is a list of experimental skills. These aren't the *only* skills you will need, just the *main* ones.

- **Design and investigate** starts by telling you how to set about solving experimental problems. Then it gives you advice on how to put your ideas into practice. Next comes a range of practical problems for you to solve. You won't find many instructions here, just a few hints to get you going. Finally, there are some bigger projects for you to try. With these, you have to do all the designing and planning yourself.

- **Questions on experimental work** gives you practice at reading the scales on meters, balances and other measuring instruments. There are also some experimental results for you to work on. You have to analyse the data and draw conclusions.

Get experimenting!

Stephen Pople

4

Experiments

Getting started

Things to remember when you are doing experiments

Be safe

Some important do's . . .

Do keep bags and coats well away from the work area, where they won't cause accidents.

Do put thermometers where they can't roll off the bench.

Do leave hot tripods and beakers to cool down before moving them.

Do leave bunsens on a yellow flame when they aren't being used, so that the flame can be seen.

Be accurate

When using a ruler: be sure that the scale is right alongside the points you are trying to measure.

When measuring the temperature of a liquid: keep the liquid well stirred, give the thermometer time to reach the temperature, keep the bulb of the thermometer in the liquid while you take your reading.

When measuring a liquid level on a scale: use the level of the flat surface, not the edge of the meniscus.

When reading a meter: be sure that you look at the pointer and scale 'square on'. Some pointers have flat ends to help you do this – check that you are looking at the point edge on.

When taking readings: take plenty! For a graph, you should take at least five sets of readings. For a single measurement, repeat at least three times and find an average value.

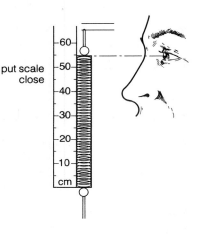

put scale close

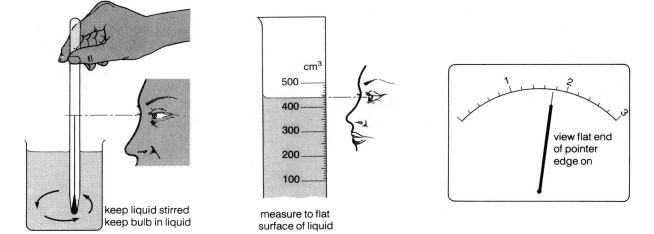

keep liquid stirred
keep bulb in liquid

measure to flat
surface of liquid

view flat end
of pointer
edge on

Record your readings

Draw a results table for your readings *before* you start your experiment. Remember to write down exactly what you are measuring and the units you are using. Put headings at the top of any columns you use.

When you take readings, put them directly in your table, *not* on a piece of scrap paper.

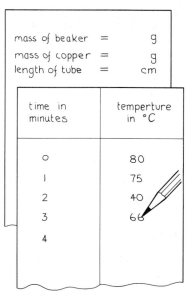

mass of beaker	=	g
mass of copper	=	g
length of tube	=	cm

time in minutes	temperture in °C
0	80
1	75
2	40
3	66
4	

Write a report

Keep it brief. Just write down:

1 the purpose of the experiment
2 what you did, and the order in which you did it
3 what measurements you had to make
4 any special precautions you took – for example, insulating and covering the beaker to cut down the loss of heat
5 any calculations you did

Draw a graph

If you have several sets of readings, you can draw a graph.

Decide which readings are going to go along the bottom axis: Usually, it's the readings you had control over. For example, if you decided to increase the force on a spring 2 newtons at a time, then force (in newtons) goes along the bottom axis.

Choose the largest scales you can for your axes: For example, 2 squares for every newton is better than 1 square for every newton – provided all the readings will fit on the graph paper. Check your highest reading before you decide on each scale.

Label your axes: Each should show what is being measured, and the units being used.

Plot the points: Most people use a small cross to mark the position of each point.

Draw the best line you can through the points: Experimental readings aren't exact, so the points will probably zig-zag a little. Don't join up the points. Decide whether the line should go through the origin. Then draw the straight line or smooth curve which goes closest to most of the points. If you've got it right, there should be roughly as many points on one side of your line as on the other.

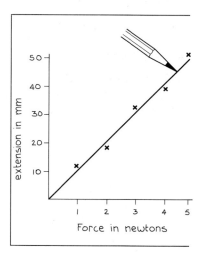

Write down your conclusions

You've done the experiment. You've written a report and plotted a graph. Finish off by writing down your conclusions – what you've found from the experiment.

Measuring the densities of solid blocks

You need:

rectangular blocks of wood, glass, iron and
    other materials

top pan balance, 0–500 g

rule marked in cm or mm

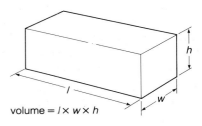

measuring mass

To measure the density of a material, you have to find its mass and
volume, then use the equation

$$\text{density in g/cm}^3 = \frac{\text{mass in g}}{\text{volume in cm}^3}$$

The mass can be measured using a top pan balance.

To find the volume of a rectangular block, you can measure its
dimensions, then use the equation

$$\text{volume in cm}^3 = \text{length in cm} \times \text{width in cm} \times \text{height in cm}$$

1 Prepare a table for your measurements, like this:

name of material	mass in g	length in cm	width in cm	height in cm	volume in cm³	density in g/cm³
wood						
glass						
Perspex						
iron						
aluminium						
copper						

volume = $l \times w \times h$

2 For each material:

  a) Measure the mass, length, width and height.
     Put these measurements in the table.

  b) Calculate the volume using the volume equation above.
     Put the result in your table.

  c) Calculate the density using the density equation above.
     Put the result in your table.

Main skills assessed:

Making measurements
Handling data
Presenting results

Measuring the density of chippings

You need:

dry chippings, 200 g approx

measuring cylinder, 0–250 cm³

top pan balance, 0–500 g

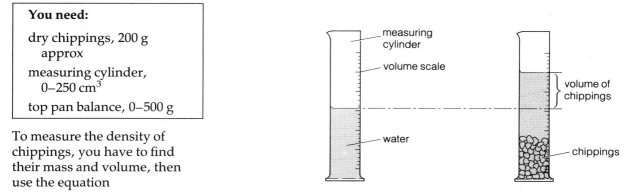

To measure the density of chippings, you have to find their mass and volume, then use the equation

$$\text{density in g/cm}^3 = \frac{\text{mass in g}}{\text{volume in cm}^3}$$

Chippings have irregular shapes, with lots of air spaces between. You need to measure the volume of the chippings and not the air spaces as well. To do this, you can empty the chippings into a measuring cylinder, partly filled with water. The chippings make the water level rise. The rise in level on the scale tells you the volume of the chippings.

1 Measure the mass of the chippings using the top pan balance. If the chippings are in a beaker, remember to take away the mass of the beaker.

2 Half-fill the measuring cylinder with water. Measure the volume of water using the scale on the side.

3 Slowly put the chippings into the water. Measure the new level on the volume scale.

4 Calculate the volume of the chippings by taking reading 2 from reading 3.

5 Calculate the density of the chippings using the equation given above.

More things to do

Also needed: sand

6 Sand has *two* density values:
the density of the grains themselves
the density, when the spaces between the grains are included.

Measure the two densities of sand.
How do the results compare?

Main skills assessed:

Making measurements
Handling data
Presenting results

Measuring the acceleration of free fall, g

You need:

steel ball	gate switch
electromagnet	clamps and stand
electronic timer	metre rule
power supply	

In this experiment, you will use an electronic timer to find how long it takes for a steel ball to fall through a measured height. The time is very short, so the timer must be able to measure accurately to within 1/100 second.

If t is the time in seconds, and h is the height fallen in metres, you can work out the acceleration of free fall, g, in metre/second^2 using the equation:

$$g = \frac{2h}{t^2}$$

The steel ball is released by pressing a switch. This cuts the power to the electromagnet *and* starts the timer. The timer stops when the steel ball strikes the gate switch and knocks it open.

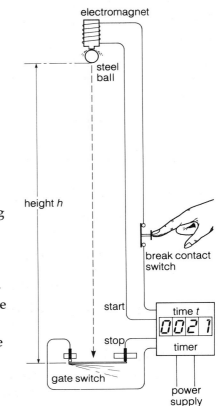

1 Set up the apparatus so that the electromagnet is about a metre above the gate switch. Check that the electromagnet will *just* hold the steel ball. Then check that the steel ball will strike the middle of the gate switch when it falls.

2 Copy out this table, ready for your readings:

h height fallen in metres	t time of fall in seconds	

3 Measure the height from the gate switch to the bottom of the steel ball. Put the result in your table.

4 Press the switch to make the ball fall. The timer will give the time of fall. Enter this reading in your table.

5 Repeat the experiment. Change the height each time, until you have five or six sets of readings.

6 Using the equation given above, calculate g from each set of readings. Use the last column of your table to record these values. Then take an average.

Main skills assessed:

Using apparatus
Handling data
Presenting results

Further work

If you have several sets of height and time measurements, the best way to find a single value of g from these is to plot a graph.

The equation on the opposite page can be rearranged like this:

$h = \frac{1}{2}gt^2$

If a graph of h against t^2 is plotted, the result should be a straight line through the origin. The gradient of the graph is $\frac{1}{2}g$.

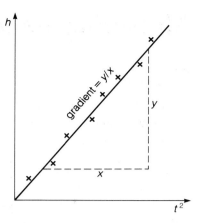

7   Use the readings in your first table to prepare a table like this:

h in metres	t^2 in s^2

8   Plot a graph of **h** (side axis) against **t^2** (bottom axis).

9   Draw the best straight line through the points. The line must pass through the origin.

10   Work out the gradient of the line. This is the value of y/x on any triangle drawn like the one in the diagram. The bigger the triangle the more accurate the result.

11   As the gradient $= \frac{1}{2}g$, it follows that $g = 2 \times$ gradient. Multiply the gradient by 2 for your value of g in m/s^2.

More things to do

12   Does the mass of the steel ball affect the value of g? Use steel balls of different masses to find out.

Another method

Another method of measuring the time of fall is to make the steel ball 'cut' through two light beams. The apparatus is shown on the right. Here, light from two small bulbs goes to two photodiodes – one at the top and one at the bottom. When you drop the ball, it briefly stops light reaching the top photodiode. This is connected to a logic gate which switches the timer *on*. When the ball gets to the bottom, it briefly stops light reaching the other photodiode. This is connected to another logic gate which switches the timer *off*.

If you are using this apparatus, work through the instructions in exactly the same order as before.

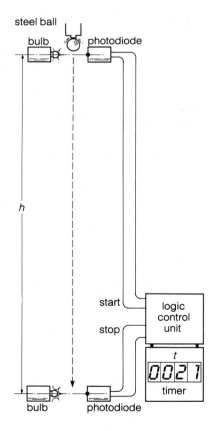

Measuring acceleration

You need:

trolley

ramp, about 2 m long

ticker timer, with 12 V a.c.
   supply

carbon paper discs

ticker-tape, about 2 m long

drawing pin, clamp or
   sticky tape

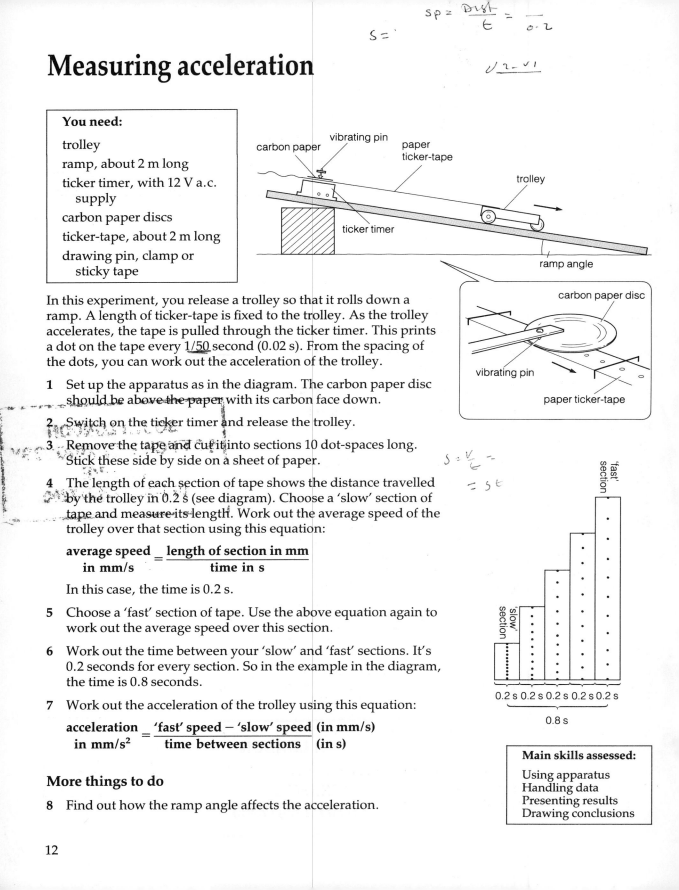

In this experiment, you release a trolley so that it rolls down a
ramp. A length of ticker-tape is fixed to the trolley. As the trolley
accelerates, the tape is pulled through the ticker timer. This prints
a dot on the tape every 1/50 second (0.02 s). From the spacing of
the dots, you can work out the acceleration of the trolley.

1   Set up the apparatus as in the diagram. The carbon paper disc
    should be above the paper with its carbon face down.

2   Switch on the ticker timer and release the trolley.

3   Remove the tape and cut it into sections 10 dot-spaces long.
    Stick these side by side on a sheet of paper.

4   The length of each section of tape shows the distance travelled
    by the trolley in 0.2 s (see diagram). Choose a 'slow' section of
    tape and measure its length. Work out the average speed of the
    trolley over that section using this equation:

$$\text{average speed in mm/s} = \frac{\text{length of section in mm}}{\text{time in s}}$$

In this case, the time is 0.2 s.

5   Choose a 'fast' section of tape. Use the above equation again to
    work out the average speed over this section.

6   Work out the time between your 'slow' and 'fast' sections. It's
    0.2 seconds for every section. So in the example in the diagram,
    the time is 0.8 seconds.

7   Work out the acceleration of the trolley using this equation:

$$\text{acceleration in mm/s}^2 = \frac{\text{'fast' speed} - \text{'slow' speed (in mm/s)}}{\text{time between sections (in s)}}$$

More things to do

8   Find out how the ramp angle affects the acceleration.

Main skills assessed:

Using apparatus
Handling data
Presenting results
Drawing conclusions

Balancing rule

You need:

metre rule
50 g masses
pencil or rod to act as a turning point or fulcrum

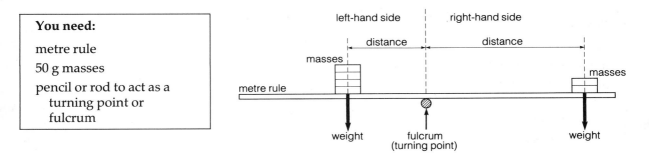

In the diagram, two stacks of 50 g masses have been placed on the metre rule. The rule balances in the middle. Each stack has a turning effect on the rule. The size of the turning effect is called a **moment**. It is calculated using the equation:

moment = weight of stack × distance from fulcrum
in N cm **in N** **in cm**

The **weight** of each stack is **1 newton (1 N)** for every **100 g** of mass.

In this experiment, you have to find out if, when the rule is balanced, there is a connection between the moment to the *left* and the moment to the *right*.

You will do this experiment several times using different masses placed in different positions along the rule.

1 Balance the rule on the fulcrum.

2 Put a mass of, say, 200 g on the left-hand side of the rule at a distance of 10 cm from the fulcrum. Then put a mass of 100 g on the right-hand side of the rule. Move it along the rule, until the rule balances. Measure the distance of the 100 g mass from the fulcrum. Put the *weights* and *distances* in a table like this:

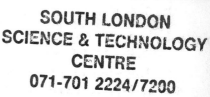

Left-hand side			Right-hand side		
weight of stack in N	distance from fulcrum in cm	moment in N cm	weight of stack in N	distance from fulcrum in cm	moment in N cm

3 Repeat the last step five or six times, using different masses in different places.

4 Compare the two columns showing the left-hand and right-hand moments. Can you draw any conclusions from your result? Write a comment about them.

Main skills assessed:

Using apparatus
Handling data
Presenting results
Drawing conclusions

Finding the centre of gravity of a piece of card

You need:

shape cut from card
clamp and stand
string
mass to hang from string

The weight of something seems to pull through one point called its **centre of gravity**. Things will balance if they are supported directly under or over their centre of gravity.

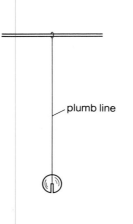

A

plumb line

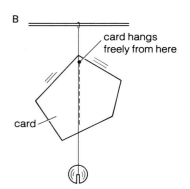

B

card hangs freely from here

card

If you hang a piece of card from a length of string, it will hang so that its centre of gravity is directly in line with the string. You can use this fact to find the position of the centre of gravity.

1   Set up the string and the mass as in diagram A. This forms a 'plumb line'; it gives an exactly vertical line.

2   Attach the piece of card to the string as in diagram B. The card must be attached to the string at one point only. It must hang freely from this point.

3   Using a pencil, and the string as a guide, mark a vertical line on the card. The centre of gravity lies somewhere along this line.

4   Hang the card from a different point as in diagram C. Draw another vertical line as before. This line will cross your first line at the centre of gravity.

5   Try hanging the card from a third point. If you have been working carefully, this should give you a third line which passes through the same point as the other two.

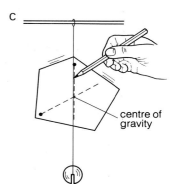

C

centre of gravity

More things to do

6   To check your result, hold the card so that it is horizontal. Then try balancing the card on an upright pencil, placed at the position you found for the centre of gravity. If you use the flat end of the pencil, the card should balance easily. If you use the pointed end, it should also balance – but not for long!

7   Find the centre of gravity of an L-shaped piece of card like the one in diagram D.

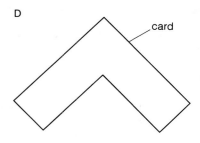

D

card

Main skills assessed:

Following instructions
Using apparatus

Stretching a spring

You need:

spring (helical)
50 g hanger and slotted masses
clamps and stand
metre rule

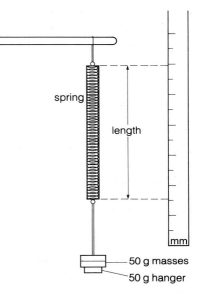

spring

length

mm

50 g masses
50 g hanger

In this experiment, you have to hang different masses from the end of a spring, and find out how much they make the spring stretch.

1 Hang the spring from the clamp.

2 Clamp the metre rule so that you can measure the length of the spring as accurately as possible.

3 Hang the 50 g hanger from the end of the spring. Measure the new length of the spring. Add 50 g masses to the hanger, one at a time, measuring the length of the spring each time. Don't use more than 300 g in total, including the hanger.

Put your results in a table like the one below. When working out the mass, don't forget to include the mass of the hanger, 50 g.

mass in g	length in mm	extension in mm

4 The **extension** of the spring is how much longer it is than its unstretched length. Complete the table by working out the extension for each set of readings in the table.

5 Describe how you arranged the metre rule so that you could measure the length of the spring as accurately as possible.

6 Plot a graph of **extension** (side axis) against **mass** (bottom axis).

7 What does the graph tell you about the way the spring stretches?

More things to do

8 Try the same experiment using a rubber band instead of a spring.

Main skills assessed:

Using apparatus
Handling data
Presenting results
Drawing conclusions

Testing the insulation of a coffee cup

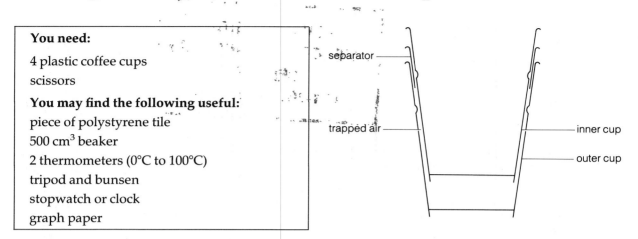

You need:

4 plastic coffee cups

scissors

You may find the following useful:

piece of polystyrene tile

500 cm^3 beaker

2 thermometers (0°C to 100°C)

tripod and bunsen

stopwatch or clock

graph paper

separator

trapped air

inner cup

outer cup

Someone thinks that they have found a better way of keeping coffee in a plastic cup warm. Their idea is that you use two cups, one inside the other. Also, you separate the two cups by the top part of a third cup, so that a layer of air is trapped between them.

Carry out an experiment to test whether this new 'double cup' loses heat more slowly than a single cup. It is probably best to fill both with hot water, rather than hot coffee. But don't use water at more than 80°C or it may damage the cups.

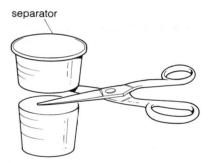

separator

1 How are you going to test which cup design insulates better?

2 If your test is going to be fair, certain things must be kept the same for both types of cup. What are they?

3 How can you make sure that virtually all the heat lost from the cups is through the sides and not from the top?

4 Carry out the test. Make a table of any readings you take.

5 Is the new cup design better? Comment on your results.

More things to do

6 Find out how an uncovered cup cools compared with a covered one.

7 Someone has suggested that a layer of aluminium kitchen foil may help to keep a cup of coffee even warmer. Test this idea by experiment.

Main skills assessed:

Designing an experiment
Handling data
Presenting results
Drawing conclusions

Measuring your power output

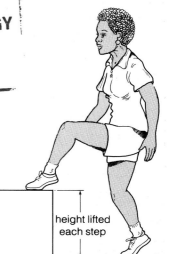

height lifted
each step

You need:

sturdy box to step on
metre rule
stopwatch
bathroom scales

To carry out this experiment, you need to know the connection between weight, force, work and power:

Let's assume you weigh 500 newtons, and you are going to climb to the top of some stairs 5 metres high. To lift yourself, you need to push upwards with a force of 500 newtons.
You will do $500 \times 5 = 2500$ joules of work.
If you take 10 seconds to make the climb, you will be doing 250 joules of work *every second*.
Your power output will be 250 watts.

In this experiment, you will be doing work by stepping up onto a box, then repeating this many times. You won't lift your bodyweight very much each time, but in total you will lift it a considerable distance.

1 Decide how you are going to measure the total height lifted. Write down what you intend to do.

2 Decide how you are going to measure the total time spent moving upwards (*not* including any time spent stepping down). Write down what you intend to do.

3 Measure your mass in kilograms. Work out your weight in newtons.

4 Start stepping! Measure the total height lifted, and the total time spent going upwards. Write these down.

5 Calculate the total work done in joules.

6 Calculate your average power output in watts.

weight in newtons	**= mass in kg**	**× 10 N/kg**
total work done in joules	**= force × distance**	
work in joules	**= weight in newtons**	**× height lifted in metres**
average power in watts	**= total work done in joules**	**time taken in seconds**

How do you compare?

Electric drill	Olympic athlete	Small car
400 watts	1000 watts	30 000 watts

Main skills assessed:

Following instructions
Handling data
Presenting results

Measuring the efficiency of a pulley

You need:

string (1 metre)
2 pulley wheels in blocks
50 g mass hangers
selection of 5 g, 10 g, and 50 g slotted masses
clamps and stand
metre rule

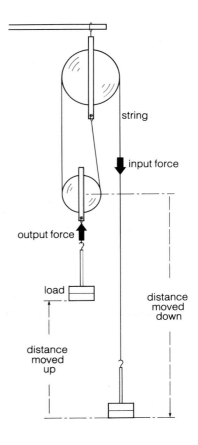

The pulley in the diagram is being used to lift a load. The force pulling the load is the output force of the system. It's 1 newton (N) for every 100 g hung from the lower pulley block.

To lift the load, there has to be a downward force on the other end of the string. This is the input force. Again, it's 1 newton for every 100 g hung from the string.

1   Set up the pulley system. Hang a mass of 100 g from the pulley (remember the hanger itself is 50 g). Start with the load on the bench, then put just enough mass on the other end of the string to make the load rise up as far as it can go.

2   Measure the distance (in mm) which the load rises up. Then measure the distance (in mm) which the masses on the string move down before they touch the bench.

3   Put your first set of mass and force results in a table like this:

mass lifted in g	output force in N	mass hung from string in g	input force in N
100	1		

4   Using the first equation on the right, calculate the work done by the output force. Remember to convert your distance measurements to metres by dividing them by 1000.

5   Using the same equation, calculate the work done by the input force.

6   Using the next equation on the right, calculate the efficiency of the pulley. Put your answer in the blank column at the end of the table.

7   Repeat steps 3, 4, 5 and 6 using larger masses each time. Put your results in the table each time.

8   Does the efficiency change? If so, how?

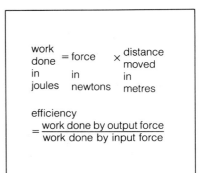

$$\begin{array}{ccc} \text{work} & & \text{distance} \\ \text{done} = \text{force} & \times & \text{moved} \\ \text{in} & \text{in} & \text{in} \\ \text{joules} & \text{newtons} & \text{metres} \end{array}$$

$$\text{efficiency} = \frac{\text{work done by output force}}{\text{work done by input force}}$$

Main skills assessed:

Using apparatus
Handling data
Presenting results
Drawing conclusions

Finding absolute zero

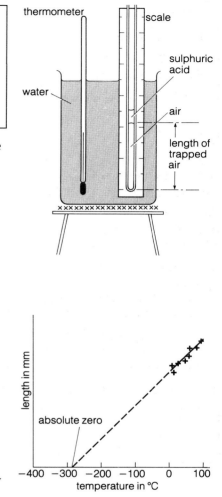

thermometer · scale
sulphuric acid
water
air
length of trapped air

You need:

narrow glass tube, containing air trapped by sulphuric acid
millimetre scale fixed to tube
500 cm beaker, thermometer (0°C–100°C)
tripod, gauze and bunsen
ice cubes

The air in the tube has been heated by the boiling water. When the air cools down, it will contract. Its volume will drop and the sulphuric acid will move down the tube. According to the kinetic theory, if the air could go on getting colder its volume would eventually drop to nothing. It would reach zero at **absolute zero**, the lowest temperature of all.

In this experiment, you measure the length of the trapped air as it cools down. From your readings you can work out how far you would have to cool the air for its volume to fall to zero. (In fact, the volume wouldn't reach zero because the gas would turn liquid.)

1 Set up the equipment as in the diagram. Heat the water over a bunsen until it is boiling gently.

2 Wait for a minute or two for the air to reach the temperature of the water. Measure the length of the trapped air and the temperature. Put your readings in a table like this:

temperature in °C	length in mm

3 Turn off the bunsen so that the water starts to cool. As the temperature drops, measure the length of the trapped air every 10°C or so. Put your readings in the table.

Remember to keep stirring the water as it cools. For quicker cooling, add ice cubes to the water.

4 Plot a graph of **length** (side axis) against **temperature** (bottom axis). Your temperature scale must cover the range from −400°C to 100°C, as shown in the diagram. Your length scale must start at zero.

5 Draw the best straight line you can through your points. Extend the line to the left, until it cuts the bottom axis. Read off the temperature where it cuts the axis. This is absolute zero.

6 Collect readings from others who have done the same experiment and work out a class average.

Main skills assessed:

Following instructions
Making measurements
Handling data
Presenting results

19

Finding the melting point of wax

You need:

paraffin wax (about 30 cm³)
boiling tube
clip for lifting boiling tube
bunsen and tripod
clamp or rack to support tube
250 cm³ beaker
thermometer (0°C to 100°C)
stopwatch or clock
graph paper

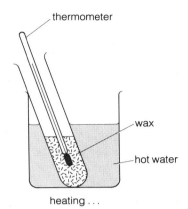

heating . . .   and cooling

The **melting point** of wax is the temperature when solid wax turns liquid if heated – or liquid wax turns solid if cooled.

In this experiment, you will melt some wax using the heat from hot water. Then you will let the wax cool so that it turns solid again. While the wax is turning back to a solid, its temperature changes hardly at all. This steady temperature is the melting point.

time in minutes	temperature in °C

1 Put the cold, solid wax in the boiling tube.

2 Partly fill the beaker with water. Put the boiling tube in the water.

3 Heat the water until all the wax has melted and its temperature is about 90°C.

4 Lift the boiling tube out of the water. Clamp it upright, well away from the bunsen.

5 Measure the temperature every half minute. Record your results in a table like the one on the right, above. Keep taking readings until the wax has completely solidified and cooled to about 40°C. **Don't** try to take the thermometer out of the solid wax.

6 Plot a graph of **temperature** against **time**, using axes like those in the diagram.

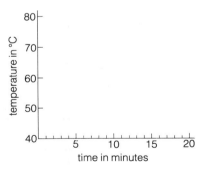

7 From the graph, read off a value for this melting point. Are there any problems in doing this?

8 Most liquids aren't single 'pure' substances. They are a mixture of different things, all with different melting points. When cooled, they turn solid over several degrees instead of at one single temperature. Look at your graph. Do you think that paraffin wax is a pure substance or a mixture of substances?

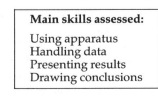

Main skills assessed:

Using apparatus
Handling data
Presenting results
Drawing conclusions

Finding the position of an image in a flat mirror

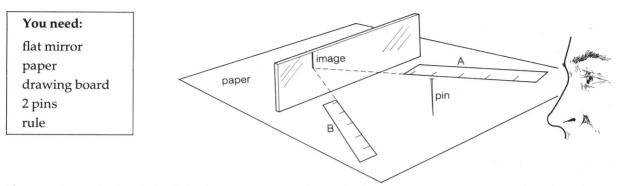

You need:

flat mirror
paper
drawing board
2 pins
rule

If you put a pin in front of a flat mirror, you see an image in the mirror. The image appears to be behind the mirror. To find its position, you have to 'point' lines at it from two different directions and find out where they meet.

1   Put the paper on the drawing board. Stand the mirror upright in the middle of the paper. Draw a line along the front of the mirror with a pencil.

2   Place a pin upright about 10 cm in front of the mirror. Mark its position.

3   Put the rule in position A. Move the rule until one edge lines up with the image of the pin. Draw a line along the edge.

4   Move the rule to position B. Again, move it until one edge lines up with the image of the pin. Draw a line along the edge.

5   Remove the pin and mirror from the paper. Extend the two lines until they cross. This is where the image seems to be.

6   Check your result like this:

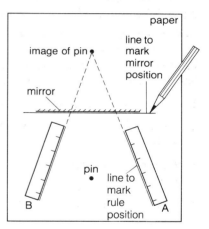

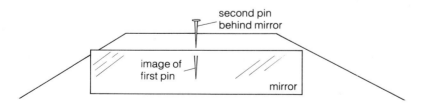

Put the mirror and the pin back into position. Hold a second pin upright behind the mirror at the point where your two lines cross. Look into the mirror. You should see the top half of this second pin exactly in line with the image of the first pin. And the pin should *stay* in line with the image even when you move your head from side to side. If it doesn't, you didn't find the image position very accurately.

Main skills assessed:

Following instructions
Using apparatus

Tracing rays through a glass block

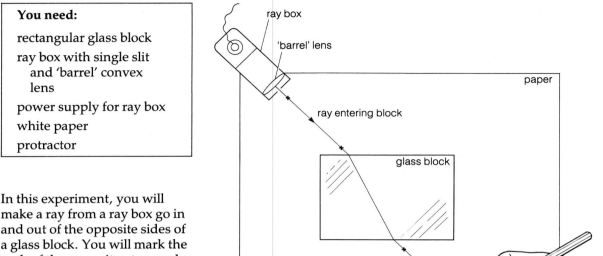

ray box
'barrel' lens
paper
ray entering block
glass block
ray leaving block

You need:

rectangular glass block
ray box with single slit
  and 'barrel' convex
  lens
power supply for ray box
white paper
protractor

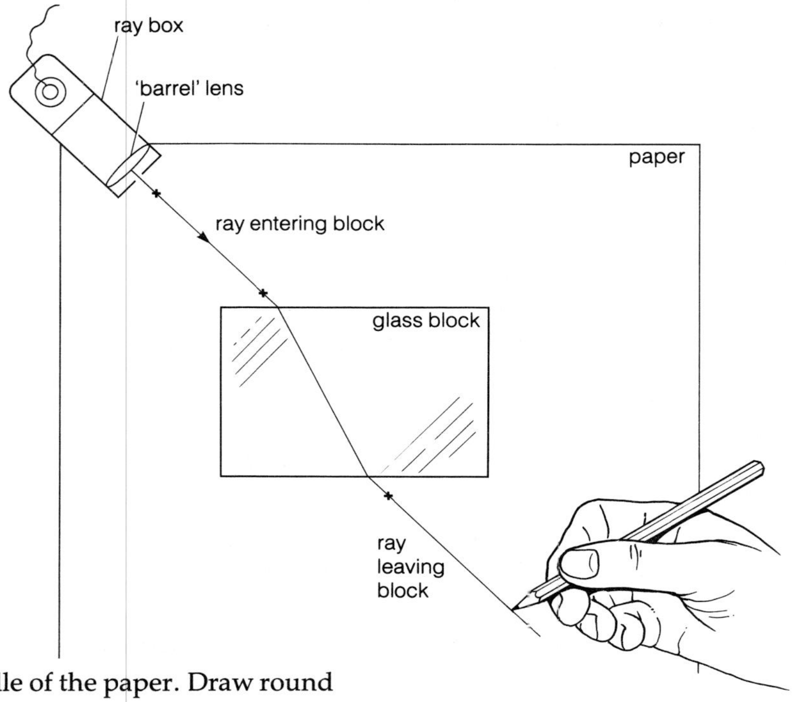

In this experiment, you will make a ray from a ray box go in and out of the opposite sides of a glass block. You will mark the path of the ray as it enters and leaves the block, and work out the path of the ray inside.

1 Place the glass block in the middle of the paper. Draw round the block to mark its position.

2 Slot the 'barrel' lens just behind the slit in the ray box. The lens makes the ray narrower and sharper.

3 Angle the ray so that it goes in and out of the block as in the diagram.

4 Using a pencil, mark the path of the ray going into the block. Two small crosses are good for this – drawn as far apart as possible. Then mark the path of the ray leaving the block.

6 Take the glass block and the ray box away. Using your crosses as a guide, draw in lines to show the path of the ray as it enters and leaves the block. Join up the lines to show the path of the ray inside the block.

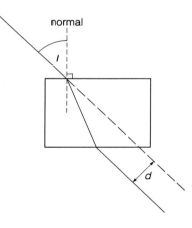

normal
I
d

More things to do

7 Measure the angle of incidence of the ray entering the block (angle I in the diagram). Then measure the distance between the paths of the rays entering and leaving the block (distance d in the diagram).

8 Repeat for at least five values of I and put your results in a table.

9 Plot a graph of d against I. Can you draw any conclusions from the graph?

Main skills assessed:

Following instructions
Handling data
Presenting results
Drawing conclusions

Tracing rays through a prism

You need:

45°–90°–45° prism (one face white)

ray box with single slit and 'barrel' convex lens

power supply for ray box

white paper

protractor

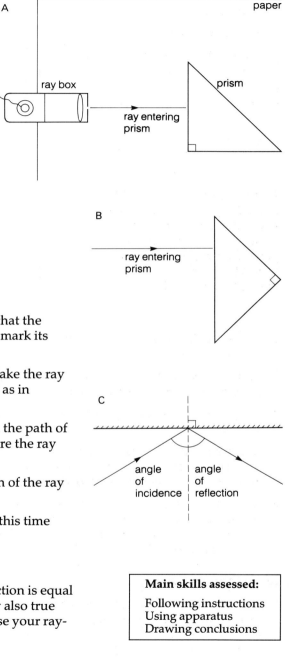

In this experiment, you pass a ray of light in and out of a right-angled prism so that it reflects off an inside face. You trace the path of the ray in much the same way as in the previous experiment with the glass block. Read through the notes on that experiment before tackling this one.

In the second part of the experiment, you change the path of the ray so that it reflects off two inside faces.

1　Place the prism in the middle of the paper. Be sure that the white face is downwards. Draw round the prism to mark its position.

2　Set up the ray box as in the previous experiment. Make the ray strike one of the short faces of the prism 'square on' as in diagram A. How can you do this accurately?

3　Mark the path of the ray going into the prism. Mark the path of the ray leaving the prism. Then mark the point where the ray reflects from the inside face of the prism.

4　Remove the prism and the ray box. Draw in the path of the ray going into, through and out of the prism.

5　Turn the paper over. Repeat the steps above – only this time make the ray meet the prism as in diagram B.

More things to do

6　When light reflects from a mirror, the angle of reflection is equal to the angle of incidence (see diagram C). Is this law also true for light reflected from the inside face of a prism? Use your ray-tracing experiments to find out.

Main skills assessed:

Following instructions
Using apparatus
Drawing conclusions

23

Measuring the critical angle of glass (or Perspex)

You need:

semi-circular glass (or Perspex) block, with one face white

ray box with single slit and 'barrel' convex lens

paper

protractor

rule

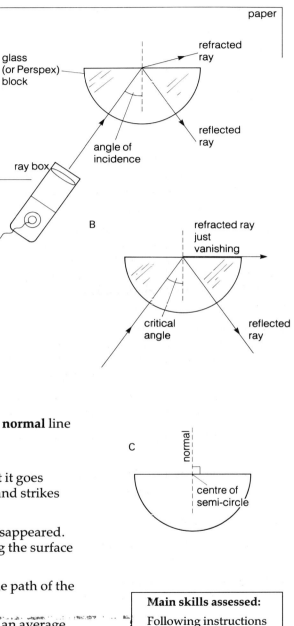

If a ray of light meets the inside face of a glass block as in diagram A, some of the light is reflected and some is refracted. Increase the angle of incidence and eventually the refracted ray will disappear as in diagram B. The angle shown is called the **critical angle**. At greater angles than this, there is no refracted ray. All the light is reflected.

In this experiment, you will measure the critical angle of glass (or Perspex). As in the previous two experiments, you will be using a ray box and drawing the path of a ray.

1   Lay the block, white face down, in the middle of the paper. Draw round the block to mark its position.

2   Find the centre of the semi-circle. Then draw in the **normal** line shown in diagram C.

3   Set up the ray box as described in the previous two experiments. Angle the ray as in diagram A, so that it goes straight through the curved face of the glass block and strikes the centre of the semi-circle.

4   Increase the angle until the refracted ray has just disappeared. Mark the position of the ray. The ray is now striking the surface of the block at the critical angle.

5   Remove the glass block and the ray box. Draw in the path of the ray. Measure the critical angle.

6   Repeat the experiment at least three times and find an average value for the critical angle.

Main skills assessed:

Following instructions
Using apparatus

Measuring the focal length of a convex lens

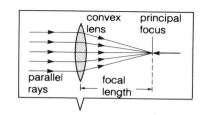

You need:

convex lens
lens holder
screen
metre rule

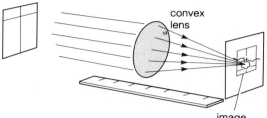

When parallel rays of light go through a convex lens, they come together at a point called the principal focus. The distance from this focus to the lens is the **focal length**.

Rays from anything a long way away are very nearly parallel. If you use a convex lens to focus rays from a distant building or tree, you can see a small image on a screen. If the image is sharp, the screen is at the principal focus. The distance from the lens to the screen is the focal length.

1 Arrange the lens, screen and metre rule as in the diagram. Light from a window must be able to pass through the lens and reach the screen. The experiment works best if the lens and screen are in the darkest part of the room, opposite the window.

2 Move the screen backwards or forwards until you see a clear image of a distant tree or building.

3 Measure the distance from the lens to the screen. This is the focal length of the lens.

4 Repeat the experiment at least three times. Find an average value for the focal length.

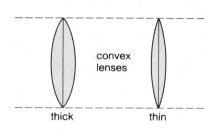

More things to do

5 Find out by experiment which has the longer focal length, a thick lens or a thin lens.

6 Find out by experiment which gives the bigger image on the screen, a thick lens or a thin lens.

Main skills assessed:

Following instructions
Using apparatus
Drawing conclusions

Finding how the depth of focus depends on aperture

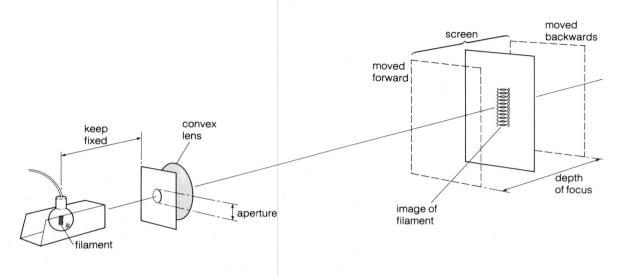

You can cut down the light going through a lens by putting a piece of card with a circular hole in it over the front. The diameter of this hole is called the **aperture**.

In this experiment you use a convex lens to focus the image of a filament on a screen. There is one screen position which will give the clearest image, but you can move the screen backwards or forwards from this position and still see an image which looks quite clear to the eye. The full distance you can move the screen is called the **depth of focus**.

Your aim is to find out how the depth of focus depends on the aperture size. To do this, you measure the depth of focus for at least five apertures.

1   Arrange the raybox, lens and screen as in the diagram. Move them until the image of the filament is about five times bigger than the filament. *Keep the distance from the lens to the ray box fixed from now on.*

2   Cut a small circular hole about 2 mm across in the card. Put this in front of the lens. Move the screen backwards until the image just starts to blur. Then move it forwards until the image blurs again. Measure the depth of focus (the distance between these two positions).

3   Cut a 4 mm hole in the card and repeat the last step. Do this again for 6 mm, 10 mm, 20 mm and 30 mm holes until the lens is fully uncovered. Put your measurements in a table like the one on the right, above.

4   What do your results tell you?

You need:

convex lens (about 30 mm aperture)

square card, large enough to cover lens

compasses, scissors

ray box (without slits)

screen

metre rule

aperture in mm	depth of focus in mm

Main skills assessed:

Making measurements
Handling data
Presenting results
Drawing conclusions

26

Measuring the speed of sound

You need:

measuring cylinder (at least 30 cm long)
glass tube (2 cm diameter at least 30 cm long)
tuning fork (frequency 288 Hz or more)
half-metre rule
clamp and stand

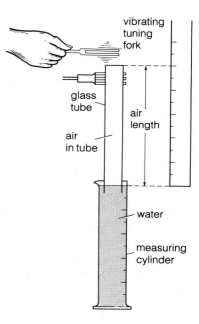

In the diagram, someone is holding a vibrating tuning fork above the air in the tube. They can change the length of the air by raising or lowering the tube. Sound waves travel through the air, and the air starts vibrating. The vibrations are strongest if the length of the air is exactly a quarter of the wavelength of the sound. This is when the air gives out its loudest note. The effect is called **resonance**. You use resonance to measure the speed of sound. If you know the frequency of the tuning fork, and can find the wavelength of the sound waves, you can calculate the speed of sound using the equation:

speed of sound = frequency × wavelength
   in m/s   **in Hz**   **in m**

1   Write down the frequency of the tuning fork. This is marked on the side of the fork.

2   Fill the measuring cylinder with water. Clamp the tube as in the diagram so that the air length is at least 30 cm.

3   Hold the vibrating tuning fork above the tube and listen. Shorten the air length by lowering the tube half a centimetre further into the water. Use the tuning fork again to see if the note you hear is louder than before. Keep doing this, checking that the note is getting louder each time. If it starts to get quieter, raise the tube again. Keep adjusting the tube until you get the loudest note. Then measure the length of the air.

4   Repeat your measurement at least four times. Find an average value for the length. Then write down that length in metres.

5   Work out the wavelength of the sound – it's four times the length of the air. Calculate the speed of sound using the equation at the top of the page.

More things to do

6   Connect a loudspeaker to a signal generator and fix it just above the top of an empty measuring cylinder. Adjust the frequency of the signal generator until resonance occurs. Measure the length of air in the measuring cylinder. Then calculate the wavelength and speed of the sound as before.

Main skills assessed:

Making measurements
Handling data
Presenting results

Measuring resistance

You need:

15 cm of nichrome wire (0.3 mm diam.)
crocodile clips, connecting wire
voltmeter to measure voltage (0–12 V)
ammeter to measure current (0–3 A)
d.c. power supply (12 V)
beaker
variable resistor (0–10 Ω)

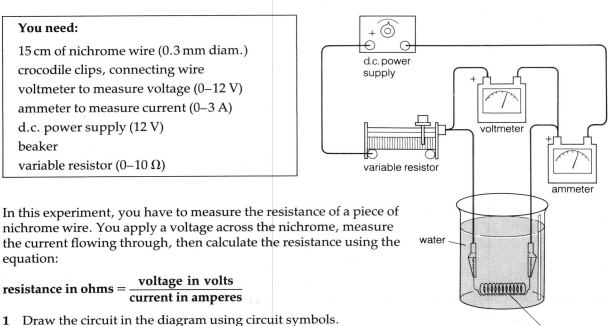

In this experiment, you have to measure the resistance of a piece of nichrome wire. You apply a voltage across the nichrome, measure the current flowing through, then calculate the resistance using the equation:

$$\text{resistance in ohms} = \frac{\text{voltage in volts}}{\text{current in amperes}}$$

1 Draw the circuit in the diagram using circuit symbols.

2 Connect up the circuit. Put the nichrome in water so that it stays cool. If the temperature of the nichrome rises, its resistance will change.

3 Adjust the d.c. supply voltage or the variable resistor so that a current of 0.5 A flows through the nichrome. Measure the voltage across the nichrome.

4 Repeat for several different current values. Enter your readings in a table like this:

current in amperes	voltage in volts	resistance in ohms

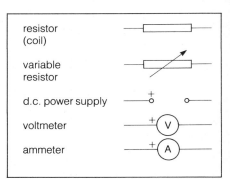

5 Complete the table by working out the resistance for each pair of readings. Do this with the equation above.

6 Comment on the resistances you have found.

More things to do

7 Switch off the current. Then take the nichrome out of the water. Switch on. Slowly increase the current until the nichrome starts to glow. Now measure its resistance. Is it more or less than it was when cool?

Measuring the current rating of a fuse

You need:

fuse (1 A approx)
ammeter (0–3 A)
bulb (12 V, 24 W)
variable resistor (0–30 Ω)
crocodile clips
connecting wire

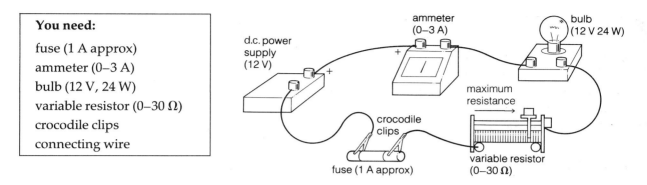

Most electrical appliances in the home have a fuse in their plug to protect the circuit. The fuse contains a thin piece of resistance wire. If a fault develops and the current rises above a certain value, the fuse 'blows'. It overheats, melts and breaks the circuit before the appliance or its cable can be damaged. A fuse with a rating of, say, 3 A will blow when a current of more than 3 A flows through. In this experiment, you have to measure the current rating of a fuse.

1   Draw the circuit using the circuit symbols on the right.

2   Set up the circuit. Check that the resistor is set for maximum resistance. Then switch on the power supply.

3   Alter the variable resistor, so that the current slowly rises. Watch the ammeter carefully – you have to note down the highest reading before the fuse blows. This is the current rating of the fuse.

4   Can you suggest ways of improving the experiment?

5   Ammeters are easily damaged if the current is too high. Explain how, in this circuit, the bulb helps protect the ammeter.

More things to do

6   Find out, by experiment, whether a long piece of fuse wire has a different current rating from a short one (of the same material and thickness).

7   Use a narrow strip of kitchen (aluminium) foil, or some strands of thin wire to make a fuse with a current rating of 1 A.

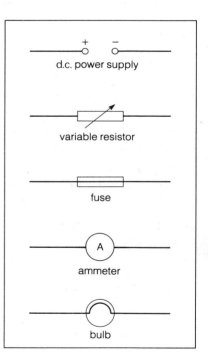

Main skills assessed:

Using apparatus
Making measurements
Drawing conclusions

Finding how current varies with voltage

Metal resistor

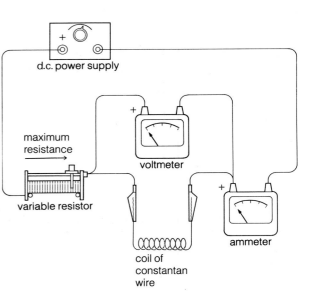

d.c. power supply

maximum resistance

variable resistor

voltmeter

ammeter

coil of constantan wire

You need:

1 metre of constantan wire (0.3 mm diam.)
crocodile clips, connecting wire
voltmeter (0–3 V)
ammeter (0–1 A)
d.c. power supply (3 V)
variable resistor (0–30 Ω)

In this experiment, you increase the voltage across a length of constantan resistance wire in stages. At each stage, you measure the current. Then you use your readings to plot a graph of current against voltage.

1   Draw the circuit in the diagram using the correct circuit symbols.

2   Connect up the circuit. Don't switch on the power supply yet.

3   Set the variable resistor for maximum resistance.

4   Alter the variable resistor (and the d.c. supply voltage) until there is a voltage of 0.5 V across the constantan. Measure the current through the ammeter.

5   Increase the voltage, 0.5 V at a time. Measure the current each time. Put your readings in a table like this:

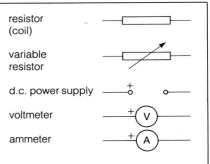

resistor (coil)

variable resistor

d.c. power supply

voltmeter

ammeter

voltage in volts (voltmeter reading)	current in amperes (ammeter reading)

6   Plot a graph of **current** (side axis) against **voltage** (bottom axis). If the points follow a curve, draw in the curve. If the points lie close to a straight line, draw in the straight line.

7   What does the graph tell you about the way the current varies with voltage?

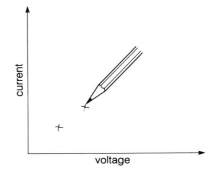

current

voltage

Light bulb filament

> **Also needed:**   small bulb (2.5 V, 0.2 A)
> bulb holder

This experiment is similar to the previous one – except that a small torch bulb is used instead of the constantan wire.

8 Carry out the experiment as before. Increase the voltage in stages up to a maximum of 2.5 V. Measure the current each time.

9 Plot a graph of current against voltage. How does this graph compare with the previous one?

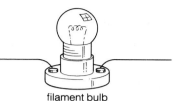

filament bulb

Semiconductor diode

> **Also needed:**   semiconductor diode (1N4001)

In this experiment, you place a semiconductor diode in the circuit instead of the light bulb.

10 Set up the circuit. Look at the marks on the diode. Make a note of which way round you have connected the diode into the circuit.

semiconductor
diode

11 Take voltage and current readings as before and put them in a table. Don't worry if one of the meters stays on zero. Just record the readings as they are. Then plot a graph of **current** against **voltage**.

Connect the diode into the circuit the other way round. Take another set of voltage and current readings. Plot another graph of **current** against **voltage**.

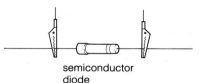

filament bulb

diode

13 Compare the two sets of results (2 and 3 above) and write a brief comment.

More things to do

14 Resistance can be calculated using the equation:

$$resistance = \frac{voltage}{current}$$

Use this equation, and readings from your graphs, to calculate the resistance of:
- the constantan wire: at 0.5 A, and at 1.0 A
- the bulb filament: at 0.1 A, and at 0.2 A
- the diode: at 0.5 A, and at 1.0 A
- the reversed diode: at 0.5 A, and at 1.0 A

> **Main skills assessed:**
>
> Using aparatus
> Making measurements
> Handling data
> Presenting results
> Drawing conclusions

Mapping the field round a magnet

You need:

bar magnet
paper
small compass

The space around a magnet where you can find its magnetism is called a **magnetic field**. If you sprinkle iron filings around a magnet, you can see the field pattern. You can also plot the field pattern using a small compass.

The field around the magnet is actually two fields – one from the magnet, the other from the Earth. The Earth's field is very weak, so it won't have much effect on your experiment if you are using a strong magnet.

1   Put the magnet in the middle of the paper. Draw round the magnet to mark its position. Keep the magnet and paper in the same place for the rest of the experiment.

2   Put a dot on the paper near one end of the magnet. Place the compass so that one end of its needle is next to the dot. Mark the position of the other end of the needle with another dot.

3   Move the compass so that the first end of the needle points to the last dot you made . . . and so on until you have a row of dots which reaches the magnet again or the edge of the paper.

4   Join up the dots with a smooth curve. You have now drawn a **field line**.

5   Repeat from a different dot by the magnet. Do this about ten times until you have drawn a full field pattern round the magnet.

More things to do

6   Find the field patterns around these magnets:

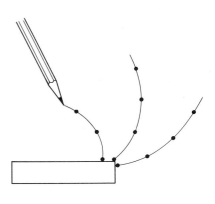

compass

paper

magnet

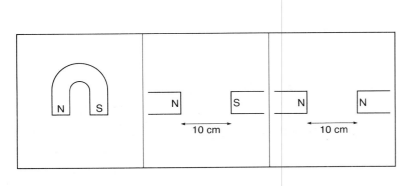

Main skills assessed:

Following instructions
Using apparatus

Testing the poles of an electromagnet

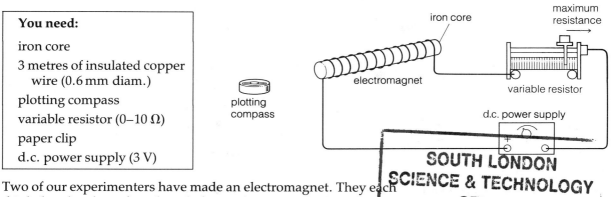

iron core

maximum
resistance

electromagnet

variable resistor

d.c. power supply

plotting
compass

Two of our experimenters have made an electromagnet. They each
think that they have found a rule for working out which end is the
N-pole. But they don't agree with each other. You have to find out
who is correct.

According to Dave's left-hand grip rule:

If you grip the
electromagnet with your
left hand, so that your
fingers point the same way
as the current, your thumb
points towards the N-pole.

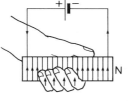

According to Tessa's right-hand grip rule:

If you grip the
electromagnet with your
right hand, so that your
fingers point the same way
as the current, your thumb
points towards the N-pole.

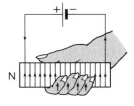

Both rules use the *conventional* current direction: the direction from
the + terminal of the battery round to the −.

1   Find out which end of the plotting compass is the N-pole and
    which is the S-pole. The N-pole is the one which points North
    when the compass is well away from other magnets.

2   Make an electromagnet by winding the wire round the core.
    Connect it to the variable resistor and power supply as in the
    diagram.

3   Set the variable resistor to give maximum resistance and switch
    on the power supply. Your electromagnet should be strong
    enough to hold a paper clip firmly. If it isn't lower the resistance
    of the variable resistor.

4   Use the plotting compass to find out which pole of the
    electromagnet is N and which is S. The N-pole of the compass is
    attracted to the S-pole of the electromagnet.

5   Carefully draw the equipment. Your diagram must show the
    direction in which the wire is wound (see diagram), the + and
    − terminals of the power supply, the (conventional) current
    direction, the N- and S-poles of the electromagnet.

6   Whose rule is correct, Dave's or Tessa's?

N-pole of
compass
points North

N-pole of compass points North

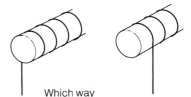

Which way
have you wound
your coil?

Main skills assessed:

Using apparatus
Making measurements
Drawing conclusions

Making an electric motor

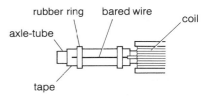

You need:

3 metres of insulated copper wire
(0.6 mm diam.)

wooden armature with axle-tube through
centre

wooden base, iron yoke, axle-rod

2 magnets, 2 split pins, 4 rivets

2 rubber rings, sticky tape

3 V d.c. power supply

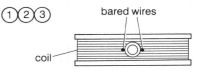

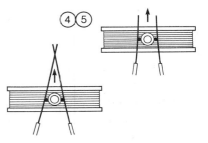

You can make a simple d.c. motor using parts from a Westminster electromagnetic kit.

1　Insulate one end of the axle-tube with tape.

2　Wind a coil of about 10 turns on the armature.

3　Strip about 2 cm of plastic from the ends of the wire. Then grip the bared ends to the axle-tube using the rubber rings. Check that the ends are opposite each other and in line with the coil.

4　Cut two half-metre lengths of wire and bare the ends. Fix the wires upright to the base using the rivets. Then put the split pins into the base.

5　Bend the two upright wires towards each other so that they just cross. Move the axle tube-upwards between them to separate them.

6　Line up the axle-tube with the split pins, and slide the axle-rod through the pins and the tube. The upright wires should now be pressing firmly against the axle-tube, and you should be able to spin the coil.

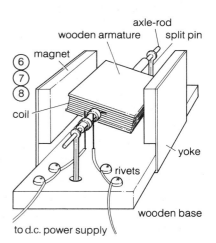

7　Put the two magnets on the yoke to make a single U-shaped magnet. Check that the opposite faces *attract* each other. Then slide the yoke into position along the base.

8　Connect the wires to power supply. Give the coil a gentle flick to start it turning.

How good is your motor?

Well-made motors will 'tick over' slowly and smoothly on a low voltage. Can you explain why? To find out if yours is the best motor, pick a challenger and connect the two motors in parallel to the *same* power supply. Slowly lower the supply voltage (you may need a variable resistor for this). The loser is the motor which stops first.

Main skills assessed:

Following instructions
Using apparatus

Measuring an a.c. voltage with an oscilloscope

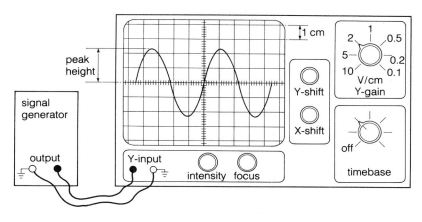

You need:

oscilloscope with
    calibrated Y-gain

signal generator, output
    5 V approx

Your source of a.c. voltage is a signal generator. This will make a wave pattern on the screen of an oscilloscope. By measuring the height of the wave pattern, you can work out the voltage of the signal generator.

Getting a wave pattern . . .

1   Connect the signal generator output to the **Y-input** terminals of the oscilloscope.

2   Turn the **Y-gain** control to a high setting; say 10 V/cm. If the oscilloscope also has a variable gain control, set this to the **calibrated** position. (Note: the gain control may be marked in V/division rather than V/cm.)

3   Switch on the signal generator and the oscilloscope. You may need to adjust the **intensity** (brightness) and **focus** controls now.

4   Turn on the **timebase** (it may be on already!). Look for a wave pattern on the screen. It will probably be the wrong size or in the wrong position or not steady, so you will have to make some adjustments:

If the height of the wave pattern is too small: adjust the Y-gain control in steps until the wave almost fills the screen.

If the wave pattern is off-centre: adjust the **Y-shift** (position) or **X-shift** controls.

If the wave pattern isn't steady: adjust the **variable timebase** control.

If the waves are too long or too short: adjust the stepped timebase control. Try to get at least two complete waves on the screen.

Measuring the a.c. voltage . . .

5   Note down the setting on the Y-gain control. For example: 2 V/cm.

6   Measure the vertical distance from the top of the wave pattern to the bottom. For example: 4.6 cm.

7   Work out the **peak height** of the waves on the screen. This is *half* your measurement in stage 6. For example:
$4.6 \times \frac{1}{2} = 2.3$ cm

8   Work out the a.c. voltage like this:

a.c. voltage = peak height × Y-gain setting
                in cm   in V/cm
For example:

a.c. voltage = 2.3 cm × 2 V/cm
          = 4.6 V

This value is called the **peak a.c. voltage**. It is the maximum voltage the signal generator produces in either the forward or the backward direction.

Main skills assessed:

Making measurements
Handling data
Presenting results

Electronic circuits

Some of the components you may use . . .

Resistors

These have a resistance in ohms (Ω). The resistance value is shown using either the colour code or the resistance code:

resistor

The colour code

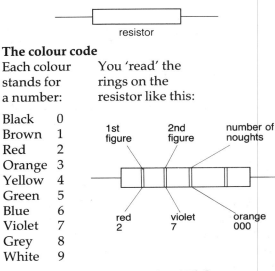

Each colour stands for a number:		You 'read' the rings on the resistor like this:
Black	0	
Brown	1	
Red	2	
Orange	3	
Yellow	4	
Green	5	
Blue	6	
Violet	7	
Grey	8	
White	9	

1st figure   2nd figure   number of noughts

red 2   violet 7   orange 000

resistance value = 27 000 Ω = 27 kΩ

The fourth ring gives the tolerance. This tells you by how much the resistance may differ from the marked value. Resistors with the gold ring are best!

Gold 5%   Silver 10%   No colour 20%

Transistors

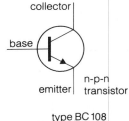

These can be used as switches. They are switched 'on' by a small voltage rather than by a lever or a button.

They have three connections:
emitter   (e)
base   (b)
collector   (c)

collector
base
emitter
n-p-n transistor
type BC 108
c   b
e

The resistance code

Resistance values are printed on the resistor:

R27 means 0.27 Ω
2R7 means 2.7 Ω
6K8 means 6.8 kΩ
47K means 47 kΩ

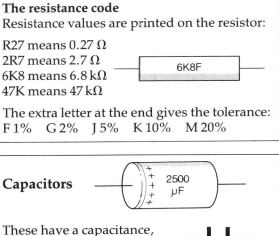

6K8F

The extra letter at the end gives the tolerance:
F 1%   G 2%   J 5%   K 10%   M 20%

Capacitors

2500 μF

These have a capacitance, usually measured in microfarads (μF).

capacitor

Electrolytic capacitors are damaged if they are connected the wrong way round. One terminal is marked + so that you know which way to make the connection.

electrolytic capacitor

S-DeC boards

These are a useful way of making up circuits without soldering. The five contact holes in each row are connected together by a copper strip underneath. You make other connections by pushing wires into the contact holes.

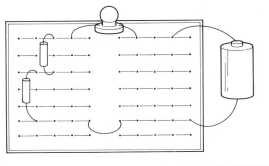

Building transistor switch circuits

Light-operated switch

You need:

n-p-n transistor (e.g. BC108)

light-dependent resistor (LDR) (type ORP 12)

d.c. power supply (6 V)

light bulb (6 V, 60 mA)

1 kΩ resistor

10 kΩ resistor

circuit board (e.g. S-DeC)

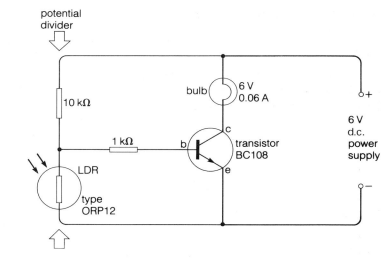

Put this circuit in a bright room and the bulb stays *off*. But cover the LDR with your hand to shield it from the light, and the bulb is switched *on*.

The bulb circuit has a transistor in it. If there is no current through its base, the transistor won't conduct, so the bulb stays off. But if the base is made positive (+), with at least 0.6 V between it and the emitter, the transistor switches on and the bulb lights up. The small voltage used to switch on the transistor comes from a voltage divider. This is made by the LDR and the 10 kΩ resistor. It passes on a share of the battery voltage to the base of the transistor.

In bright daylight, the LDR has a low resistance. It passes on a low share of the battery voltage – not enough to switch the transistor on.

When the LDR is put in the dark, its resistance rises. Now it passes on more than the 0.6 V needed to switch on the transistor. So the bulb lights up.

1   Connect up the circuit, leaving the power supply disconnected. When you have had your circuit checked, make the final connection to the power supply.

> **Wiring problems?**
> Draw the circuit out in pencil.
> Connect one small section of circuit at a time.
> Draw over that section of your diagram in pen so that you can see what's left to be done.

2   Shield the LDR from light with your hand. What happens?

3   Swap over the LDR and the 10 kΩ resistor. How does this affect the way the circuit behaves?

light-dependent resistor (LDR)

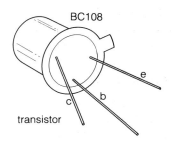

transistor

Main skills assessed:

Following instructions
Using apparatus

Light-operated switch with relay

Also needed:
magnetic relay (6–17 V, 185 Ω)
electric bell (6 V)
diode (OA202)

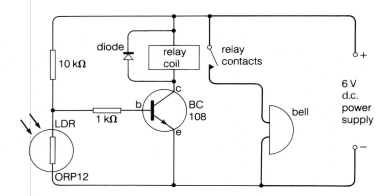

A transistor can switch a small light bulb on or off without any problem. But it can't take the current needed to make, say, an electric bell work. One way over this difficulty is to use a type of magnetic switch called a **relay**. The relay, which can take higher currents, switches on the bell.

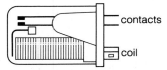

relay connections

To protect the transistor, a diode must be connected across the relay coil. Without the diode, the transistor would be damaged by the high voltage generated when the relay coil is switched off.

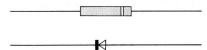

diode

1 Connect up the circuit, leaving the power supply disconnected. Check that the diode is the right way round. Have your circuit checked. Then connect the power supply.

2 Shield the LDR with your hand. What happens?

Heat-operated switch

Also needed:
thermistor (TH3)
variable resistor (0–1 kΩ)

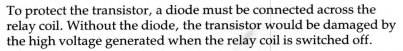

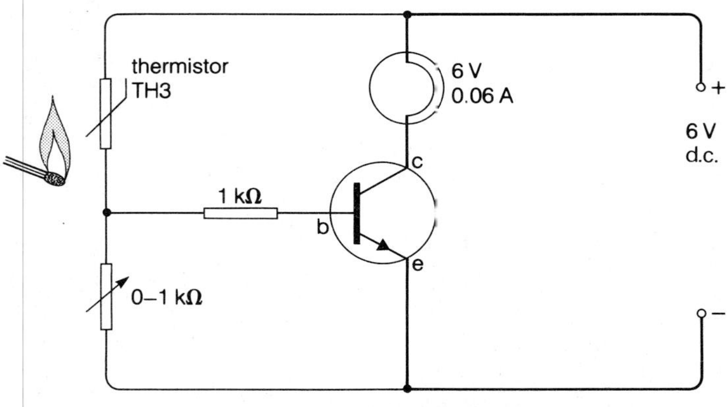

A thermistor is a heat-sensitive resistor. It has a high resistance when cold and a low resistance when hot.

Just like a LDR, it can be used in a transistor switch circuit. In this case however, it is heat which switches the circuit on, not light.

1 Connect up the circuit. Have it checked. Alter the variable resistor so that the bulb lights up when you hold a lighted match near the thermistor.

2 Change the circuit to include a relay and bell.

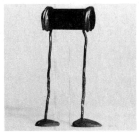

Design and investigate

Design an experiment . . .

On the following pages there are several problems for you to solve experimentally. Each time, you have to design an experiment, carry it out, and arrive at a conclusion. Read through the following before you start each one:

Planning your experiment

- *Make a list of the equipment you are going to use.*
  We've given some suggestions with each problem set. You don't have to use all of this apparatus. You don't even have to use any of it. You may have better ideas of your own.

- *Decide what things you need to measure and write them down.*
  If, say, you are going to make measurements on a swinging pendulum, you might decide to measure the following quantities:

  length of pendulum in cm
  time in seconds

- *Decide which things shouldn't change during the experiment.*
  If you are going to change the length of a pendulum, don't change the mass as well. You can't handle too many changes at once! Concentrate on finding out how *one* factor affects just *one* other.

- *Check that your experiment is a 'fair' test.*
  If, say, you are going to find out how a silver saucepan loses heat compared with a black one, check the following:

  Are both saucepans the same size?
  Do they both have a lid?
  Do they both have the same mass of hot water in them?
  Are they both starting at the same temperature?
  And if not, does it matter?

- *Make a plan of what you are going to do.*
  Describe what you are going to do. Your description needn't be very long. But be sure it covers the following:

  The problem you are trying to solve.
  A list of the apparatus you are going to need.
  A labelled diagram of your experiment.
  What measurements you are going to make.
  How you are going to make sure that the test is fair.

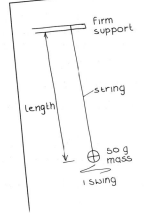

Carrying out the experiment

If your teacher has checked your plan, you can carry out the experiment:

- **Follow your plan step by step.**
  Make a note of any problems you come across or changes you have to make.

- **Put your readings in a table.**
  Examples of tables are shown on the right. When taking readings:

  Do use headings in your table (e.g. length, temperature).
  Do include the units (e.g. cm, °C).
  Do take at least *six* pairs of readings if you are going to plot a graph.
  Do write readings straight in your table.
  Don't put your readings on scrap paper.

Presenting your results

When your experiment is complete, you need to write a brief report on what you have done. You already have a written plan, so just add any *extra* information:

- **Describe any problems you came across.**
  Did you have difficulty making any of the measurements accurately?
  What problems did you meet?
  How did you overcome them?

- **Include** all **your readings.**

- **Include any graphs you have plotted.**
  When you take pairs of readings, you *choose* which values to give one of the quantities – like choosing to measure the time at 1, 2, 3 minutes, and so on. Usually, this quantity goes along the bottom axis of the graph.

  Remember to label both axes of each graph.

- **Show any calculations you have done.**

- **Write a comment about what you found.**
  Did you solve the problem? What result did you find?

- **Suggest how you might improve the experiment if you did it again.**

You may need a table for your readings like this:

mass of block   =   g
volume of block =   cm
temperature   =   °C

Or you may have several sets of readings. If so, they will need to be written in a table like this:

length in cm	time in seconds

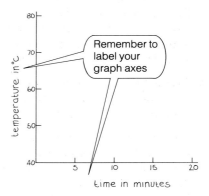

Wet or dry?

The makers of a well known brand of soft tissue paper claim that their tissues are just as strong wet as dry. Are they right? Design and carry out an experiment to test their claim.

Start by thinking about the following:
What is meant by the 'strength' of a tissue?
Do you need to measure the strength of a whole tissue?
How can you make sure that the test comparing wet and dry tissues is fair?

You need:

soft paper tissues

You might need:
mass hanger
slotted masses, 5 g to 50 g
beaker
wire
string
bulldog clips
teat pipette

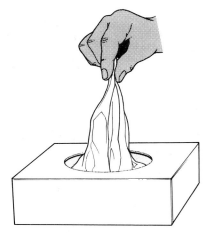

Measuring a page

Design and carry out experiments to measure

a) the thickness of one page of a book
b) the mass of one page of the book
c) the density of the paper used in the book

You mustn't damage the book in any way!

Note: $\text{density} = \dfrac{\text{mass}}{\text{volume}}$

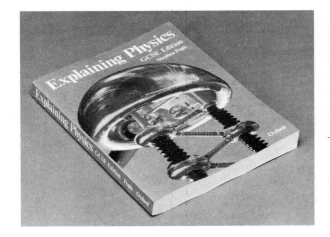

You need:

book
top pan balance, half-metre rule

Fine or coarse?

Coarse glasspaper ('sandpaper') rubs through a wooden surface more quickly than fine glasspaper. But does it produce more friction? You have to find out by experiment.

Start by thinking about the following:
How can you measure the frictional force when glasspaper is rubbed on wood?
How can you keep the glasspaper pressed against the wood?
Will the force used to press the glasspaper against the wood affect the result?
How can you make sure that the test comparing the two types of glasspaper is fair?

You need:

fine glasspaper, coarse glasspaper
wooden board

You might need:
wooden blocks, drawing pins
string, pulley
mass hanger and masses, 5 g–50 g

Bouncing ball

Some table tennis balls have more 'bounce' than others. Design and carry out a test to compare the bounce of two table tennis balls.

Start by thinking about the following:
What is meant by bounce?
What do you need to measure?
How can you make sure that the test comparing the balls is fair?

Further experimental work:

Do different bat surfaces affect the bounce?
Does the bounce of a table tennis ball depend on its star rating?

You need:

table tennis balls of different grades
table tennis bat

You might need:
metre rule, clamps and stand

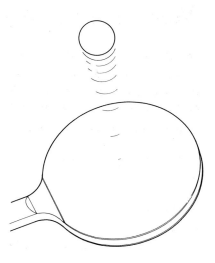

Shortest distance

Place a bright object well away from a convex lens as in the diagram, and you can get a clear image on a screen. If you move the object closer, the position of the image also changes. You need to move the screen to get a clear image again.

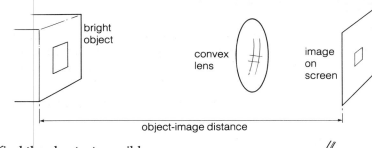

Design and carry out an experiment to find the shortest possible distance between the object and its image.

Further work

Is there a connection between the focal length of a lens and its shortest possible object-image distance? Do experiments with several lenses to find out. (There's an experiment for measuring the focal length of a lens on page 25.)

You need:

selection of convex lenses (maximum focal length 25 cm)
bright object e.g. illuminated 'square' as in the diagram
screen, metre rule, graph paper

Size and distance

Place a bright object well away from a convex lens as in the diagram, and you can get a clear image on a screen. If you move the object closer, the size and the position of the image both change. You need to move the screen to get a clear image again.

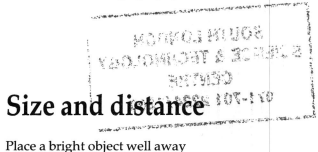

Is there a connection between the size of the image and its distance from the lens? Design and carry out an experiment to find out.

You need:

convex lens, focal length approx 15 cm
bright object e.g. illuminated 'square' as in the previous experiment
screen, metre rule, graph paper and sticky tape

Apparent depth

The person in the diagram is looking at a pin on the bottom of a beaker of water. Light from the pin gets refracted (bent) when it leaves the water. As a result, the water looks less deep than it really is and the pin appears closer to the surface than it really is.

Design and carry out an experiment to find the apparent depth of some water in a beaker.

Start by thinking about the following:
If you look at a pin in some water, it is an *image* of the pin which you are seeing. You have to find the exact position of this image. Then you have to measure the distance from the image to the water surface.

Further work

Is there a connection between the *apparent* depth of water and its *actual* depth? Try experiments with different depths of water to find out?

You need:

beaker, pins, half-metre rule, card, clamps and stand

Unknown mass

Design and carry out an experiment to find the mass of a lump of Plasticine (or some other solid).

You aren't allowed to use a balance with a mass scale already marked on it. And you aren't allowed to use slotted masses of less than 50 g.

You need:

lump of Plasticine, mass unknown, but between 50 g and 200 g

You might need:
spring (helical)
50 g hanger and slotted masses
clamps and stand
metre rule
string

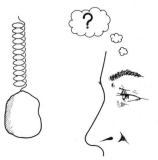

Small mass

In the last experiment, you worked out a method of finding the mass of a lump of Plasticine. Now, take the problem a stage further. Design and carry out an experiment to measure a much smaller mass – such as the mass of a pen or pencil.

This time, you can use a selection of standard masses down to 5 g.

Start by thinking about the following:
One of the problems with your last design is that it probably won't be sensitive enough to measure a small mass.
But can it be modified in any way?
Is there a different or unusual way of setting up the apparatus so that it is more sensitive to smaller masses?

You need:

small mass – such as a pen or a pencil

You might need:
spring (helical)
standard masses of 5 g, 10 g and 20 g
clamps and stand, metre rule, string

Two pairs or one?

People claim that two pairs of socks are warmer than one. But is it true? Does the extra pair cut down the heat loss? Design and carry out an experiment to find out.

You don't have to put the socks over warm feet. Some other source of heat will do.

Start by thinking about the following:
How are you going to tell that one thing is losing heat more rapidly than another?
How are you going to make sure that your test is fair?

You need:

2 socks

You might need:
beakers, thermometers, stopwatch or clock

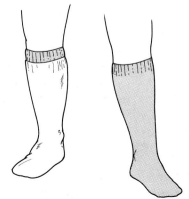

Double glazing

People often fit double glazing in their houses because two layers of glass, with air between, are supposed to lose heat more slowly than a single layer. But does double glazing cut down heat loss? Design and carry out an experiment to find out.

Start by thinking about the following:
How are you going to set up a double layer of glass with air between?
What are you going to use as a source of heat?

How are you going to tell whether less heat flows when the extra layer of glass is added?
How are you going to make sure that your test is fair?

Further work

In some double-glazed windows, one of the glass sheets has a thin transparent metal coating. The makers claim that the coating cuts heat losses even more.

Find out the effects of placing a sheet of shiny metal between your two layers of glass. Aluminium kitchen foil is a convenient metal to use in your experiment – though it isn't of course suitable for use in windows.

You might need:
glass plates, glass beakers, thermometers, stopwatch or clock insulating material, aluminium foil

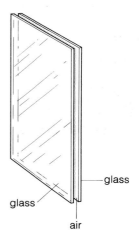

glass

glass

air

Tube volume

Design and carry out an experiment to measure the volume of glass in a boiling tube.

Start by thinking about the following:
Are you going to measure the volume directly, or calculate it from other measurements? Would it be useful to find the 'inside' and 'outside' volumes of the tube first?

You need:

boiling tube

You might need:
half-metre rule, string, measuring cylinder

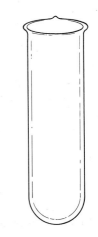

Salt on ice

During winter, salt is often sprayed on the roads to melt the ice. Pure ice has a **melting point** of 0°C; this is the temperature at which ice changes to liquid. Adding salt to ice affects the melting point.

Design and carry out an experiment to find out *how* the melting point of ice changes when salt is mixed in.

Find out if there is a connection between the melting point and the concentration of salt in the ice. If there is, show the connection in the form of a graph.

Start by thinking about the following:
How you can make sure that the salt and ice are properly mixed?
How are you going to measure the melting point?
How are you going to measure the concentration of salt in the ice?
Hint: give the concentration in grams of salt per centimetre cubed of ice.

You need:

ice, salt

You might need:
thermometer (reading down to −20°C)
test tubes, top pan balance, measuring cylinder (0–50 cm³)

Resistor

Resistors are used for keeping voltages and currents at correct levels in electronic circuits. You can make a resistor from nichrome wire.

Make a resistor with a resistance of 5 Ω.

Start by thinking about the following:
How does the length of wire affect its resistance?
How is resistance calculated?
What circuit are you going to use to make measurements?
From your measurements, how can you work out how much wire you need?

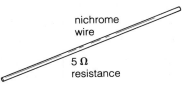

nichrome wire

5 Ω resistance

You need:

nichrome wire 0.3 mm diam.

You might need:
crocodile clips, connecting wire
d.c. power supply (3 V), voltmeter, ammeter, variable resistor

Rubber band

Postex Ltd want to market a cheap spring balance for measuring the weight of letters. Their designer suggests that, to save money, they could use a rubber band instead of a spring. Their technician says that this wouldn't be any good, because rubber bands change length and 'springiness' once they've been stretched. Who is correct? Design and carry out an experiment to find out.

Further work

Can you find out by experiment whether a rubber band is brand new or whether it has been stretched before?

You need:

supply of unused rubber bands

You might need:

slotted masses and hangers, string, metre rule, clamp and stand, graph paper

Marking time

Your teacher will play you a series of 'beeps' or other sounds at regular intervals. You won't be told the time between them, but it will always be the same – and somewhere between 2 and 10 seconds.

You have to design and carry out an experiment to measure the time between the beeps. While the beeps are being sounded, you *won't* be allowed to use a stopwatch – though you *can* use a clock while developing your experimental method.

Start by thinking about the following:
What are you going to use to 'count' time?
Will it keep a regular 'beat'?
How are you going to check it against a stopwatch or clock?

You might need:

stopwatch or clock
small masses, string, metre rule, graph paper
burette, beaker, measuring cylinder

Pendulum

The time of one complete swing of a pendulum is called its **period**.

There are some factors which *might* affect the period of swing:

the mass of the bob
the size (**amplitude**) of the swing
the length of the pendulum

Design and carry out an experiment to find out which of these factors does affect the period.

Start by thinking about the following:
The period of your pendulum will probably be a couple of seconds at most.
How are you going to find the time of one swing accurately?
How are you going to measure the size of the swing?

Note: you must make sure that the top of the pendulum string is firmly held so that there is no movement at that point.

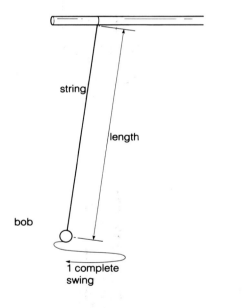

Further work

Find out how the period of one pendulum compares with another one which is four times as long (you could choose lengths of 20 cm and 80 cm for example).
Is there a simple connection between the length and the period?
Does the connection work for other lengths as well?

You need:

pendulum bobs (50 g slotted masses), string, metre rule, stopwatch or clock, clamps and stands.

Room temperature

Design and carry out an experiment to measure the temperature of the room you are in.

You aren't allowed to use a ready-made thermometer to take the measurement. But you *can* use a thermometer while developing your experimental method.

You can use the following information:

temperature of melting ice; 0°C
temperature of boiling water; 100°C

Start by thinking about the following:
You need something which will respond to a temperature change. What measurements will you need to make on it?
How can you use these measurements to work out the temperature of the room?

You might need:

thermistor, battery, milliammeter, ice, beaker
bimetal strip, half-metre rule
thermometer (0°C–100°C)
graph paper

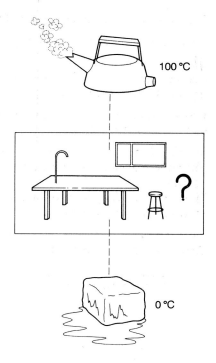

100°C

?

0°C

Further investigations

Infrared control

Many TVs and video recorders can be controlled by remote hand-held controllers. These work by sending out a beam of infrared radiation. Investigate the factors which affect the range of the controller. These could include distance, angle and the presence of reflecting surfaces.

Heat in the loft

In winter, it is important to stop the temperature of water pipes in the loft falling below freezing. One possible way of doing this is to put a light nearby to provide some heating. Investigate the effectiveness of different kinds of light as frost preventers. These could include filament bulbs, fluorescent lights and ultraviolet lights.

Hot bodies

When you exercise, your body temperature changes. So does your skin temperature. Investigate the effect of exercise on skin temperature.

Near point

The near point is the closest point you would normally hold a book in front of you for relaxed, strain-free reading. Investigate whether there is a connection between a person's nearpoint and their age.

Background radiation

Many natural materials contain tiny amounts of radioactive substances. These cause background radiation. Investigate the background radiation coming from a range of natural materials. The materials could include soil, fertilizers and different types of rock.

Sound-proofing

Sounds pass more easily through some materials than others. And some frequencies are more easily transmitted than others. Investigate the properties of a range of sound-proofing materials.

Energy conserved

The law of conservation of energy states that when energy changes into a different form, the total quantity of energy doesn't change. Design and carry out an experiment to test this law.

Electromagnetic detecting

Use a range of detectors to investigate the different types of electromagnetic radiation present in the laboratory.

Falling 'chutes

Using small models, investigate the factors affecting the rate of fall of a parachute.

Questions on experimental work

What are they reading?

There are six instruments on this page. Copy and complete the table, giving the name of each instrument and the reading it shows. The first one is done for you.

	instrument	reading
1	stopwatch	10 s
2		
3		
4		
5		
6		

1

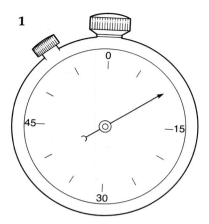

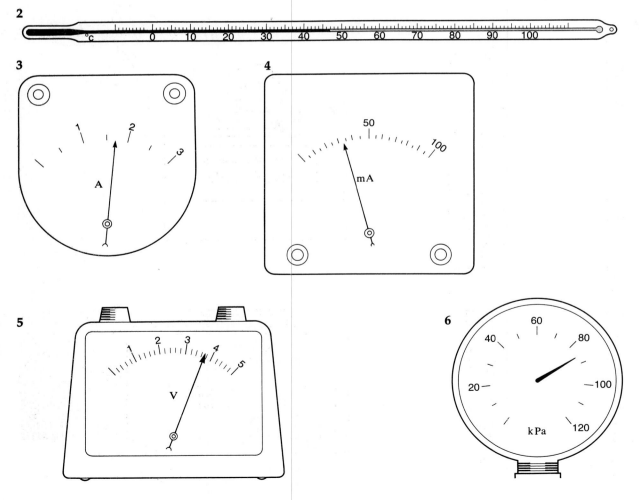

2

3

4

5

6

More instruments

There are six instruments on this page. Write down the name of
each one and the reading it shows.

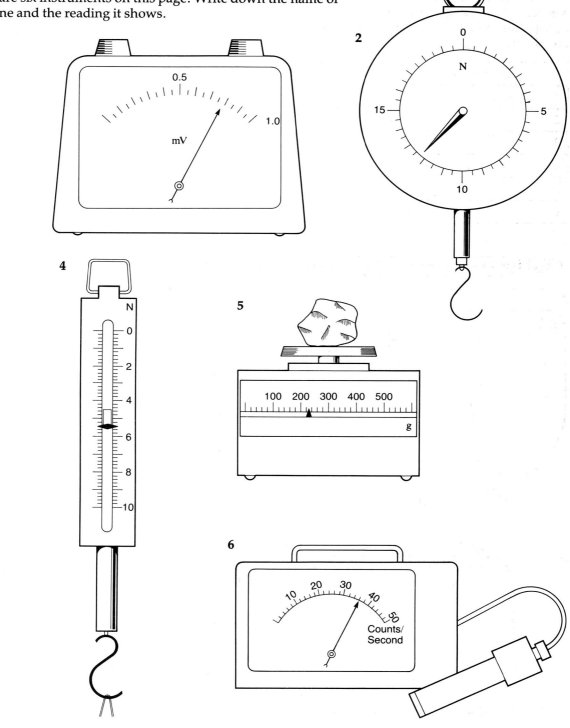

1

0.5

1.0

mV

2

0

N

15

5

10

3

4

N

0

2

4

6

8

10

5

100   200   300   400   500

g

6

10   20   30   40   50

Counts/
Second

Length and area

To answer some of the questions on this page, you will need a ruler worked in millimetres.

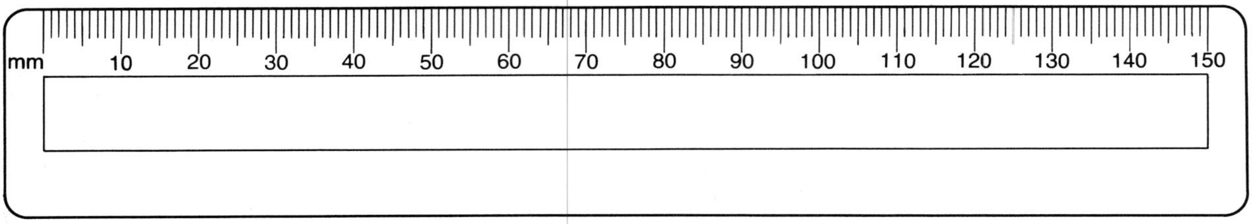

1 What is the length of each of these rods in mm?

A

B

C

D

2 What is the area of this microscope slide in mm^2?

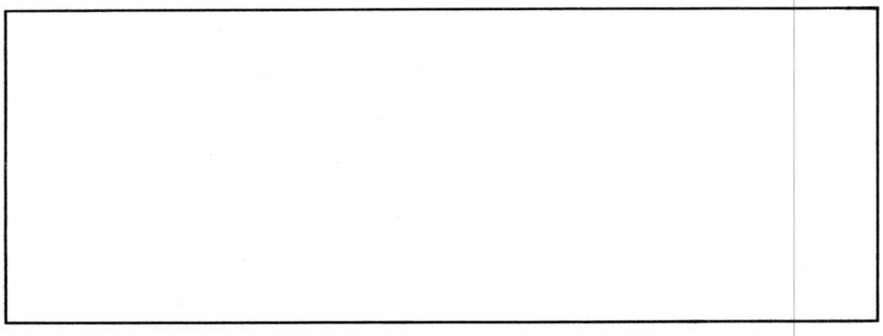

3 Which of these shapes has the largest area? Which has the smallest area?

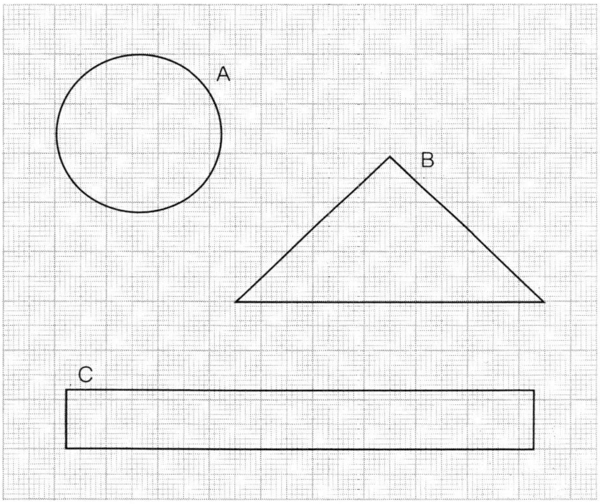

A

B

C

4 How far does this ball move when it falls to the floor?

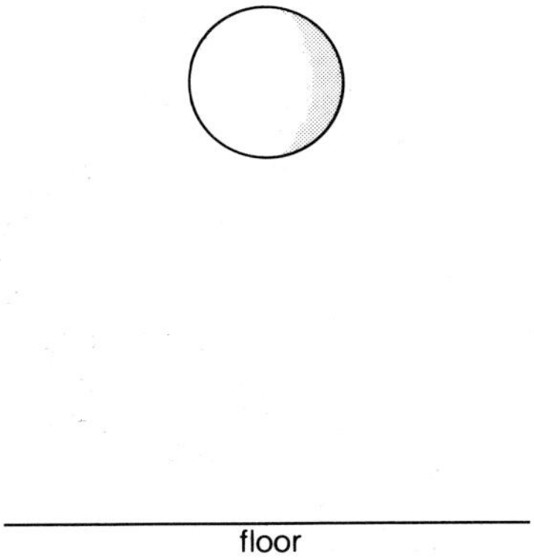

floor

5 When the spring in the diagram has been stretched, how much longer is it than when it started?

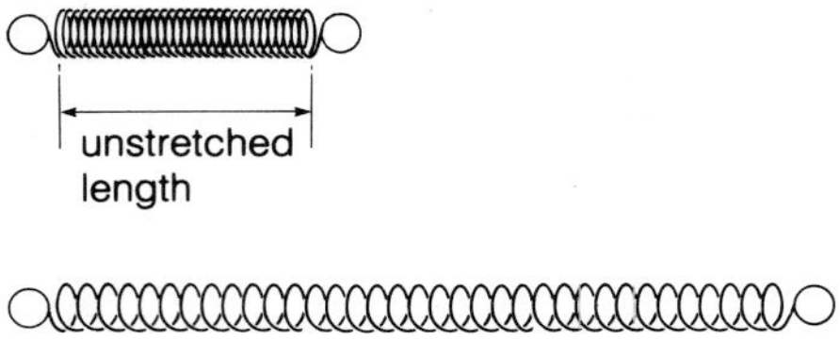

unstretched length

More measurements

To answer some of these questions, you will
need a ruler marked in millimetres.

1   What is the wavelength of these waves?

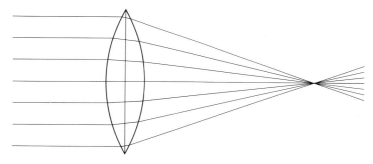

2   What is the focal length of this lens?

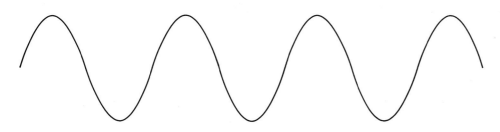

4   What is the volume of the
liquid in this measuring
cylinder?

3   What is the amplitude of the wave trace on
this oscilloscope screen?
What is the peak voltage of the input signal?

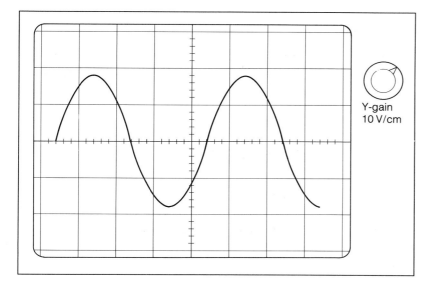

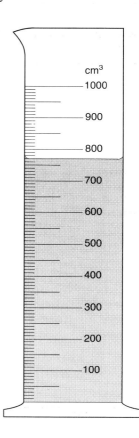

What's the pressure?

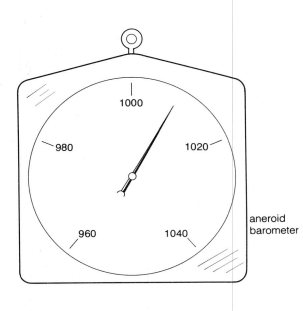

aneroid barometer

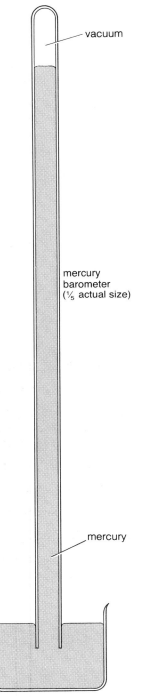

vacuum

mercury barometer (⅕ actual size)

mercury

1 Sue has an aneroid barometer in the hall at home. It measures atmospheric pressure in *millibars*. Sue suspects that the barometer isn't reading accurately, so she decides to check it against the mercury barometer in her school laboratory. She thinks of two ways of doing this:

    a) Taking her barometer to the laboratory and comparing the two instruments side by side.

    b) Ringing the laboratory to find out the reading on their barometer, then checking the reading against hers.

    Which should she choose? Why is the other method not a good idea?

2 What is the reading (in millibars) on the aneroid barometer in the diagram?

3 If the mercury barometer in the diagram is *one fifth* actual size, what is its reading? (Use a ruler marked in millimetres to make the measurement, and give the pressure reading in millimetres of mercury.)

4 Work out whether the two barometers are giving the same pressure reading.

    (Comparing pressure units:
1 millibar = 0.75 mm of mercury)

What's the density?

Julie wants to find the densities of a pebble and a cube of wood. She makes some measurements in the laboratory:

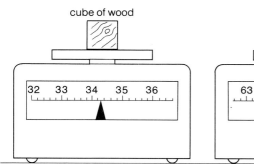

cube of wood

pebble

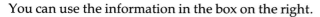

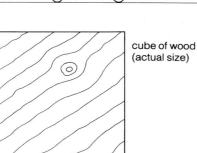

cube of wood
(actual size)

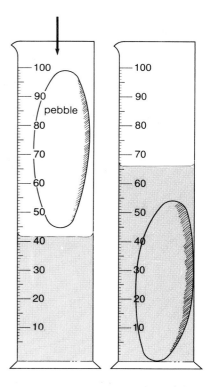

You can use the information in the box on the right.

1 What is the mass of the cube in g?

2 The cube in the diagram is shown actual size.
   Measure it using a ruler.
   What is the volume of the cube in cm^3?

3 What is the density of the cube in g/cm^3?

4 What is the mass of the pebble in g?

5 What is the volume of the pebble in cm^3?

6 What is the density of the pebble in g/cm^3?

7 Julie thinks that the pebble is made of granite. Could she be
   right? Give two reasons why she can't be certain about her
   conclusion.

$$\text{density in } g/cm^3 = \frac{\text{mass in g}}{\text{volume in } cm^3}$$

material	density in g/cm^3
graphite	2.3
quartz	2.6
clay	2.6
agate	2.6
granite	2.7
slate	2.8

Hoist efficiency

Sue uses a hoist to lift her motorcycle engine from the floor to her workbench. To lift the engine upwards, she has to pull a rope downwards. She decides to measure the efficiency of the hoist. These are the measurements she makes:

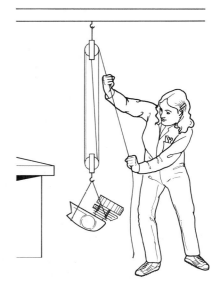

mass of engine	=	14 kg
height of bench	=	0·9 m
downward force or rope	=	30 N
number of pulls on rope	=	9
distance moved each pull	=	0.6 m
time taken to lift engine	=	12 s

You can use the equation given on the right to answer these questions.

1. What is the weight of the engine in newtons?

2. What force is used to lift the engine?

3. How much work is done in lifting the engine from floor to bench?

4. Sue measures the downward force she uses on the rope. Suggest how she can do this.

5. What is the *total* distance the rope is pulled downwards?

6. What is the *total* work done on the rope?

7. Why are your answers to questions 3 and 6 not the same?

8. What is the efficiency of the hoist?

9. What is the power output of the hoist?

10. What is the power input by Sue?

$$\text{weight of each kg on Earth} = 10 \text{ N}$$

$$\underset{\text{in J}}{\text{work}} = \underset{\text{in N}}{\text{force}} \times \underset{\text{in m}}{\text{distance moved}}$$

$$\underset{\text{in W}}{\text{power}} = \frac{\text{work in J}}{\text{time in s}}$$

$$\text{efficiency} = \frac{\text{work output}}{\text{work input}}$$

$$= \frac{\text{power output}}{\text{power input}}$$

Heating water

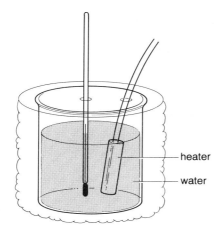

heater

water

Mei Lai is using a small electrical heater to heat some water in a beaker. She measures the power of the heater, the mass of the water, and the temperature of the water every 2 minutes. Her readings are in the table on the right.

To answer these questions, you can use the equations given at the bottom of the page.

1 Draw a circuit diagram to show how Mei Lai should connect the heater. How could she measure the power of the heater?

2 Plot a graph of **temperature** (side axis) against **time** (bottom axis).

3 Describe in words what happens to the temperature of the water during the experiment.

4 What is the highest temperature reached by the water? Why doesn't the temperature rise above this value?

5 From the graph, work out how long it takes the water temperature to rise from 20°C to 70°C.

6 Calculate the energy supplied by the heater in this time.

7 Calculate the energy needed to heat the water by 1°C. Then calculate the energy needed to heat 1 kg of water through 1°C.

8 In a separate experiment, Joanne takes the readings shown on the right. Use these readings to plot another graph, using the same axes as before. Give *two* possible reasons why Joanne's graph is different from Mei Lai's.

power	= voltage × current
in W	in V in A

energy	= power × time
in J	in W in s

Mei Lai

mass of water = 100 g

power of heater = 35 W

time in minutes	temperature in °C
0	17
2	28
4	37
6	47
8	58
10	67
12	76
14	86
16	95
18	100
20	100

Joanne

time in minutes	temperature in °C
0	17
2	32
4	45
6	58
8	71
10	84
12	96
14	100
16	100

Echoes

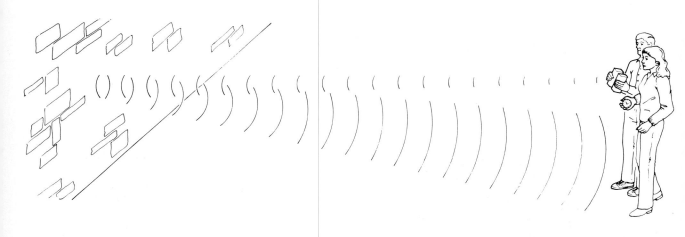

Two students stand well back from a brick wall. Craig claps two wooden blocks together. Anil uses a stopwatch to measure the time between the clap and the echo. Their readings are shown on the right.

distance from wall in m	time between clap and echo in s
50	0.35
75	0.45
100	0.65
125	0.75
150	0.95
175	1.10
200	1.25

1 Plot a graph of **time** (side axis) against **distance** (bottom axis).

2 Explain why the graph goes through the origin (0, 0).

3 Use the graph to work out the time between clap and echo when the two students are standing 160 metres from the wall.

4 How far does the sound go during this time?

5 Using your graph and this equation:

$$\text{speed in m/s} = \frac{\text{distance in m}}{\text{time in s}}$$

calculate the speed of sound in air.

6 Why is the experiment less accurate for shorter distances?

7 Why is it difficult for Anil to measure the echo time accurately?

8 How could Anil make a more accurate measurement of the time, still using the same stopwatch?

9 Sound goes more slowly on a cold day than on a warm one. Draw a sketch of your graph – showing just the shape of the line and the axes. Then draw another sketch to show how the graph would be different if the air temperature were to fall.

Resistance

nichrome wire

Wayne wants to measure the resistance of some nichrome wire. He remembers that resistance can be calculated using this equation:

$$\text{resistance in ohms} = \frac{\text{voltage in volts}}{\text{current in amperes}}$$

Using a circuit, he puts different voltages across a piece of nichrome wire and measures the current flowing through each time. His readings are on the right.

1   Draw a diagram of the circuit he should use to take these readings.

2   Explain how he can change the voltage.

3   Plot a graph of **current** (side axis) against **voltage** (bottom axis.)

4   Explain how you can tell from the graph that the resistance of the nichrome doesn't change.

5   Use your graph to work out the resistance of the nichrome wire.

6   a) Draw a small sketch of the graph – showing just the shape of the line and the two axes.
    b) Draw a second sketch to show how the graph would have looked if the nichrome wire had been longer.
    c) Draw a third sketch to show how the graph would have looked if the nichrome wire had been thicker.

Wayne does a second experiment with a tungsten filament bulb instead of the nichrome wire. His readings from this experiment are on the right.

7   Plot a graph of **current** (side axis) against **voltage** (bottom axis).

8   Explain why this graph is a different shape from the graph for nichrome.

9   Calculate the resistance of the filament when the current is
    a) 1.0 A   **b)** 2.0 A
    What has happened to the resistance?

nichrome wire

voltage in V	current in A
1.0	0.08
2.0	0.16
3.0	0.26
4.0	0.33
5.0	0.42
6.0	0.50

tungsten filament

voltage in V	current in A
1.0	0.9
2.0	1.4
3.0	1.8
4.0	2.1
5.0	2.3
6.0	2.5

Answers

What are they reading? (p. 54)
1 10 s   **2** 47°C   **3** 1.7 A   **4** 33 mA   **5** 3.7 V
6 87 kPa

More instruments (p. 55)
1 0.79 mV   **2** 12.4 N   **3** −14°C   **4** 5.4 N
5 230 g   **6** 36 counts/s

Length and area (p. 56)
1 A: 39 mm   B: 73 mm   C: 26 mm   D: 56 mm
2 2400 mm^2 **3** C, A   **4** 34 mm   **5** 33 mm

More measurements (p. 57)
1 35 mm   **2** 50 mm   **3** 18 mm, 18 V   **4** 770 cm^3

What's the pressure? (p. 58)
1 A   **2** 1008 mb   **3** 770 mm (1027 mb)

What's the density? (p. 59)
1 34.3 g   **2** 42.9 cm^3 **3** 0.8 g/cm^3 **4** 64.8 g
5 24 cm^3 **6** 2.7 g/cm^3 **7** yes

Hoist efficiency (p. 60)
1 140 N   **2** 140 N   **3** 126 J   **5** 5.4 m   **6** 162 J
8 78%   **9** 10.5 W   **10** 13.5 W

Heating water (p. 61)
4 100°C   **5** 10 minutes   **6** 21 000 J
7 420 J, 4200 J

Echoes (p. 62)
3 1.03 s   **4** 320 m   **5** 320 m/s

Resistance (p. 63)
5 12 Ω   **9 a)** 1.2 Ω   **b)** 1.8 Ω

Index

Acknowledgements

Photography by Peter Gould and Chris Honeywell
Diagrams by Mike Ing, Impulse Graphics